GW01086878

Treble Clef Brass
Scales, Arpeggios & Exercises

for Trinity College London
exams from 2015

Grades 1-8

Published by:
Trinity College London
www.trinitycollege.com

Registered in the UK
Company no. 02683033
Charity no. 1014792

Photo: Zute Lightfoot, trumpet courtesy of Yamaha Music London

Printed in Great Britain by Caligraving Ltd.

Contents

Introduction

This book contains all the scales, arpeggios and exercises listed in Trinity's Brass syllabus for treble clef brass readers except French horn, trombone and soprano cornet. French horn players may use the publication *French Horn Scales, Arpeggios & Exercises Grades 1–8 from 2015*. Treble clef trombone players may use the publication *Trombone Scales, Arpeggios & Exercises Grades 1–8 from 2015*. Documents giving the technical work required for soprano cornet are available to download from www.trinitycollege.com/music

At each grade you will find the lip flexibility exercises (section i), scales & arpeggios (section ii) and the exercises (section iii, Grades 1–5 only) which may be presented as an alternative to scales. In the exam, exercises can be played from the music while lip flexibility exercises and scales must be performed from memory.

Lip flexibility exercises, besides being extremely useful for sound and stamina development, also make excellent warm-ups and the use of different exercises chosen from across the grades will help all students in their daily practice. Advanced students are encouraged to extend the range of the early exercises when using them as warm-ups. The fingerings given are for three-valve instruments. Players with a fourth valve should naturally substitute that in place of 1st and 3rd.

The scales are presented grouped by key and arranged from C–B. The syllabus has been devised in a way which will develop a deepening understanding of tonal centres. The range and complexity of material to be learnt within a given tonal centre increases with each grade.

The exercises (in section iii, which may be presented in place of scales), are based on the same tonal centres as the scales. Candidates preparing the scales are advised also to practise the exercises to help familiarise themselves with the tonal centres. Candidates presenting the exercises will also benefit from practising the scales.

The tempo ranges shown in the book are taken from the syllabus and are intended to cover all brass instruments; technical work should be prepared at a consistent speed appropriate to the instrument. For most instruments, scales and arpeggios should be prepared in a single breath; where an extra breath is necessary this should be taken in a musically logical place, usually at the top of the exercise. For the purposes of fulfilling exam criteria, accuracy, fluency and evenness of tone should be regarded as equally important aspects of technical competence.

Candidates are advised always to check the current syllabus for exact requirements of the exam.

Grade 1

Candidate to prepare i) Lip flexibility exercise				
Lip flexibility exercise (from memory) Play the exercise slurred, using the valve combinations given.				
Candidate to prepare in full *either* section ii) *or* section iii)				
either **ii) Scales & arpeggios** (from memory) − the examiner will select from the following:				
Scales: C major A minor (candidate's choice of natural *or* harmonic *or* melodic minor) **Arpeggios:** C major A minor	one octave	♩= 46-60	tongued	*mf*
or **iii) Exercises** (music may be used)				
Candidate to prepare 1a *or* 1b; 2a *or* 2b; and 3a *or* 3b (three exercises in total). The candidate will choose one exercise to play first; the examiner will then select one of the remaining two prepared exercises to be performed.				
1a. Let's Play! *or* 1b. Threesy-peasy		for finger technique		
2a. March to the Top *or* 2b. The Football Chant		for articulation		
3a. I am an Elephant *or* 3b. Creeping		for breath control *or* rhythm		

i) Lip flexibility exercise

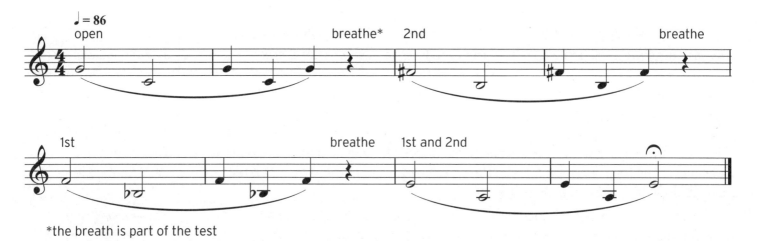

*the breath is part of the test

ii) Scales & arpeggios

C major scale (one octave)

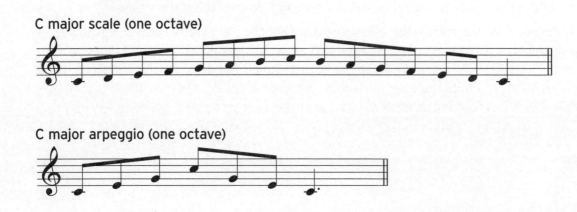

C major arpeggio (one octave)

A natural minor scale (one octave)

A harmonic minor scale (one octave)

A melodic minor scale (one octave)

A minor arpeggio (one octave)

iii) Exercises

1a. Let's Play! – finger technique

1b. Threesy-peasy – finger technique

2a. March to the Top – articulation

2b. The Football Chant – articulation

3a. I am an Elephant – breath control

3b. Creeping – rhythm

Grade 2

Candidate to prepare i) Lip flexibility exercise				
Lip flexibility exercise (from memory) Play the exercise slurred, using the valve combinations given.				
Candidate to prepare in full *either* section ii) *or* section iii)				
either **ii) Scales & arpeggios** (from memory) – the examiner will select from the following:				
Scales: D and B♭ major D minor (candidate's choice of natural *or* harmonic *or* melodic minor)	one octave	♩=50-66	tongued *or* slurred as requested by the examiner	*mf*
Arpeggios: D and B♭ major D minor				
or **iii) Exercises** (music may be used)				
Candidate to prepare 1a *or* 1b; 2a *or* 2b; and 3a *or* 3b (three exercises in total). The candidate will choose one exercise to play first; the examiner will then select one of the remaining two prepared exercises to be performed.				
1a. Hand-bell Peal *or* 1b. Calypso and So		for finger technique		
2a. Lolloping *or* 2b. Sneakers		for articulation		
3a. Eastern Promise *or* 3b. Jumper		for breath control *or* rhythm		

i) Lip flexibility exercise

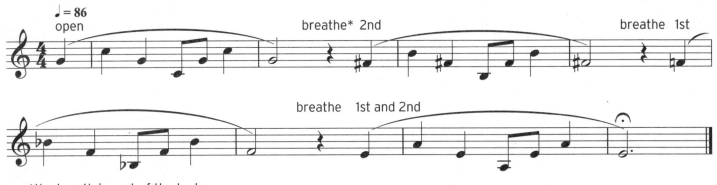

*the breath is part of the test

ii) Scales & arpeggios

D major scale (one octave)

D major arpeggio (one octave)

8

D natural minor scale (one octave)

D harmonic minor scale (one octave)

D melodic minor scale (one octave)

D minor arpeggio (one octave)

Bb major scale (one octave)

Bb major arpeggio (one octave)

iii) Exercises

1a. Hand-bell Peal – finger technique

(lower notes for tuba)

1b. Calypso and So – finger technique

2a. Lolloping – articulation

2b. Sneakers – articulation

3a. Eastern Promise – breath control

3b. Jumper – rhythm

Grade 3

Candidate to prepare i) Lip flexibility exercise				
Lip flexibility exercise (from memory) Play the exercise slurred, using the valve combinations given.				
Candidate to prepare in full *either* section ii) *or* section iii)				
either **ii) Scales & arpeggios** (from memory) − the examiner will select from the following:				
Scales: E and E♭ major C and C♯ minor (candidate's choice of *either* harmonic *or* melodic minor)	one octave	♩ = 54-72	tongued *or* slurred as requested by the examiner	*mf*
Whole-tone scale starting on C				
Arpeggios: E and E♭ major C and C♯ minor				
or **iii) Exercises** (music may be used)				
Candidate to prepare 1a *or* 1b; 2a *or* 2b; and 3a *or* 3b (three exercises in total). The candidate will choose one exercise to play first; the examiner will then select one of the remaining two prepared exercises to be performed.				
1a. Let's Rock! *or* 1b. Ambling Along		for low note tonguing *or* finger technique		
2a. Stately Dance *or* 2b. Mouse Meets Elephant		for articulation		
3a. Jigsaw Peace *or* 3b. The Sleepwalking Robot		for breath control		

i) Lip flexibility exercise

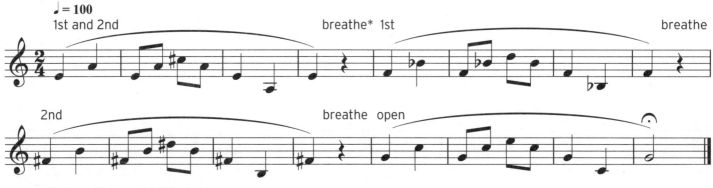

*the breath is part of the test

ii) Scales & arpeggios

C harmonic minor scale (one octave)

C melodic minor scale (one octave)

C minor arpeggio (one octave)

Whole-tone scale starting on C (one octave)

C# harmonic minor scale (one octave)

C# melodic minor scale (one octave)

C# minor arpeggio (one octave)

E♭ major scale (one octave)

E♭ major arpeggio (one octave)

E major scale (one octave)

E major arpeggio (one octave)

iii) Exercises

1a. Let's Rock! – low note tonguing

1b. Ambling Along – finger technique

(lower notes for tuba only)

2a. Stately Dance – articulation

*(lower note for tuba only)

2b. Mouse Meets Elephant – articulation

Grade 3 continued

3a. Jigsaw Peace – breath control

*(breath only for low brass)

3b. The Sleepwalking Robot – breath control

Grade 4

<table>
<tr><td colspan="5">Candidate to prepare i) Lip flexibility exercise</td></tr>
<tr><td colspan="5">Lip flexibility exercise (from memory)
Play the exercise slurred, using the valve combinations given.</td></tr>
<tr><td colspan="5">Candidate to prepare in full either section ii) or section iii)</td></tr>
<tr><td colspan="5">either ii) Scales & arpeggios (from memory) − the examiner will select from the following:</td></tr>
<tr>
<td>Scales:
F and A major
F and F♯ minor (candidate's choice of either harmonic or melodic minor)

Whole-tone scale starting on F
Chromatic scale starting on C

Arpeggios:
F and A major
F and F♯ minor</td>
<td>one octave</td>
<td>♩ = 60-104</td>
<td>tongued or slurred as requested by the examiner</td>
<td>mf</td>
</tr>
<tr><td colspan="5">or iii) Exercises (music may be used)</td></tr>
<tr><td colspan="5">Candidate to prepare 1a or 1b; 2a or 2b; and 3a or 3b (three exercises in total).
The candidate will choose one exercise to play first; the examiner will then select one of the remaining two prepared exercises to be performed.</td></tr>
<tr><td colspan="4">1a. Rescue Squad   or   1b. Bob-tail Bob</td><td>for finger technique</td></tr>
<tr><td colspan="4">2a. Let in Latin   or   2b. After the Battle</td><td>for articulation</td></tr>
<tr><td colspan="4">3a. Balloon Ride   or   3b. Sliding Down the Banister</td><td>for breath control</td></tr>
</table>

i) Lip flexibility exercise

Grade 4 continued

ii) Scales & arpeggios

Chromatic scale starting on C (one octave)

F major scale (one octave)

F major arpeggio (one octave)

F harmonic minor scale (one octave)

F melodic minor scale (one octave)

F minor arpeggio (one octave)

Whole-tone scale starting on F (one octave)

F# harmonic minor scale (one octave)

F# melodic minor scale (one octave)

F# minor arpeggio (one octave)

A major scale (one octave)

A major arpeggio (one octave)

iii) Exercises

1a. Rescue Squad – finger technique

1b. Bob-tail Bob – finger technique

2a. Let in Latin – articulation

2b. After the Battle – articulation

3a. Balloon Ride – breath control

3b. Sliding Down the Banister – breath control

*(breath only for low brass)

Grade 5

Candidate to prepare i) Lip flexibility exercise				
Lip flexibility exercise (from memory) Play the exercise slurred, using the valve combinations given.				
Candidate to prepare in full *either* section ii) *or* section iii)				
either **ii) Scales & arpeggios** (from memory) – the examiner will select from the following:				
Scales: G major G minor (candidate's choice of *either* harmonic *or* melodic minor)	two octaves	♩ = 66–112	tongued *or* slurred as requested by the examiner	*mf*
A♭ major B and E minor (candidate's choice of *either* harmonic *or* melodic minor)	one octave			
Whole-tone scale starting on G Chromatic scale starting on G	two octaves			
Arpeggios: G major G minor				
A♭ major B and E minor	one octave			
Dominant 7th in the key of G				
or **iii) Exercises** (music may be used)				
Candidate to prepare 1a *or* 1b; 2a *or* 2b; and 3a *or* 3b (three exercises in total). The candidate will choose one exercise to play first; the examiner will then select one of the remaining two prepared exercises to be performed.				

1a. Jump Start	*or*	1b. Ta Aunt Ella!	for octave leaps *or* finger technique
2a. Tongue-go	*or*	2b. Cheeky Chops	for articulation
3a. Smooth Strides	*or*	3b. Finding the Pulse	for breath control *or* rhythm

i) Lip flexibility exercise

*(breath only for tuba)

Repeat (descending) using the following valve combinations:

2nd – 1st – 1st and 2nd

ii) Scales & arpeggios

E harmonic minor scale (one octave)

E melodic minor scale (one octave)

E minor arpeggio (one octave)

G major scale (two octaves)

G major arpeggio (two octaves)

G harmonic minor scale (two octaves)

G melodic minor scale (two octaves)

G minor arpeggio (two octaves)

Chromatic scale starting on G (two octaves)

Grade 5 continued

Whole-tone scale starting on G (two octaves)

Dominant 7th in the key of G (one octave)

A♭ major scale (one octave)

A♭ major arpeggio (one octave)

B harmonic minor scale (one octave)

B melodic minor scale (one octave)

B minor arpeggio (one octave)

iii) Exercises

1a. Jump Start – octave leaps

1b. Ta Aunt Ella! – finger technique

2a. Tongue-go – articulation

2b. Cheeky Chops – articulation

(lower notes for tuba)

3a. Smooth Strides – breath control

3b. Finding the Pulse – rhythm

Grade 6

Candidate to prepare i) Lip flexibility exercise and chromatic scale					
Lip flexibility exercise (from memory) Play the exercise slurred, using the valve combinations given. Chromatic scale starting on A (two octaves, from memory) (tempo, dynamics and articulation as for scales below)					
Candidate to prepare in full _either_ section ii) _or_ section iii)					
either **ii) Scales & arpeggios** (from memory) − the examiner will select from the following:					
Candidates should prepare scales and arpeggios from the following tonal centres: A major, A minor A♭ major, G♯ minor	two octaves	♩=72-120	tongued, slurred _or_ staccato-tongued as requested by the examiner	_f_ or _p_	
Plus: Whole-tone scale starting on A♭ Dominant 7th in the key of D♭ Diminished 7th starting on A Augmented arpeggio starting on A					

When the examiner requests a **major tonal centre**, the candidate should play in succession:
    The major scale
    The major arpeggio
 	
When the examiner requests a **minor tonal centre**, the candidate should play in succession:
    The melodic minor scale
    The harmonic minor scale
    The minor arpeggio					

_or_ **iii) Orchestral and brass band extracts** See current syllabus for details					

i) Lip flexibility exercise and chromatic scale

Repeat (descending) using the following valve combinations:

1st − 2nd and 3rd − 1st and 3rd

Chromatic scale starting on A (two octaves)

ii) Scales & arpeggios

Dominant 7th in the key of D♭ (two octaves)

A♭ major scale (two octaves)

A♭ major arpeggio (two octaves)

G#/A♭ harmonic minor scale (two octaves)

G#/A♭ melodic minor scale (two octaves)

G#/A♭ minor arpeggio (two octaves)

Whole-tone scale starting on A♭ (two octaves)

Grade 6 continued

A major scale (two octaves)

A major arpeggio (two octaves)

A harmonic minor scale (two octaves)

A melodic minor scale (two octaves)

A minor arpeggio (two octaves)

Augmented arpeggio starting on A (two octaves)

Diminished 7th starting on A (two octaves)

Grade 7

<table>
<tr><td colspan="5">Candidate to prepare i) Lip flexibility exercise and chromatic scale</td></tr>
<tr><td colspan="5">Lip flexibility exercise (from memory)
Play the exercise slurred, using the valve combinations given.

Chromatic scale starting on B (two octaves, from memory) (tempo, dynamics and articulation as for scales below)</td></tr>
<tr><td colspan="5">Candidate to prepare in full either section ii) or section iii)</td></tr>
<tr><td colspan="5">either ii) Scales & arpeggios (from memory) – the examiner will select from the following:</td></tr>
<tr>
<td>Candidates should prepare scales and arpeggios from the following tonal centres:
B major, B minor
Bb major, Bb minor

Plus:
Chromatic scale starting on Bb
Whole-tone scale starting on B and Bb
Dominant 7th in the keys of E and Eb
Diminished 7th starting on B and Bb
Augmented arpeggio starting on B and Bb</td>
<td>two octaves</td>
<td>♩ = 80-126</td>
<td>tongued, slurred or staccato-tongued as requested by the examiner</td>
<td>f or mf
or p or
cresc./dim.
(p-f-p)
or
dim./cresc.
(f-p-f)</td>
</tr>
<tr>
<td colspan="5">When the examiner requests a major tonal centre, the candidate should play in succession:
    The major scale
    The major arpeggio

When the examiner requests a minor tonal centre, the candidate should play in succession:
    The melodic minor scale
    The harmonic minor scale
    The minor arpeggio</td>
</tr>
<tr>
<td colspan="5">or iii) Orchestral and brass band extracts
See current syllabus for details</td>
</tr>
</table>

i) Lip flexibility exercise

Repeat (descending) using the following valve combinations:

1st − 1st and 2nd − 1st and 3rd

Tuba only:

Repeat (descending) using the following valve combinations:

1st − 2nd and 3rd − 1st, 2nd and 3rd

Grade 7 continued

Chromatic scale starting on B (two octaves)

ii) Scales & arpeggios

Dominant 7th in the key of E♭ (two octaves)

Dominant 7th in the key of E (two octaves)

B♭ major scale (two octaves)

B♭ major arpeggio (two octaves)

B♭ harmonic minor scale (two octaves)

B♭ melodic minor scale (two octaves)

B♭ minor arpeggio (two octaves)

Chromatic scale starting on B♭ (two octaves)

Whole-tone scale starting on B♭ (two octaves)

Augmented arpeggio starting on B♭ (two octaves)

Diminished 7th starting on B♭ (two octaves)

B major scale (two octaves)

Grade 7 continued

B major arpeggio (two octaves)

B harmonic minor scale (two octaves)

B melodic minor scale (two octaves)

B minor arpeggio (two octaves)

Whole-tone scale starting on B (two octaves)

Augmented arpeggio starting on B (two octaves)

Diminished 7th starting on B (two octaves)

Grade 8

<table>
<tr><td colspan="5">Candidate to prepare i) Lip flexibility exercise and chromatic scale</td></tr>
<tr><td colspan="5">Lip flexibility exercise (from memory)
Play the exercise slurred, using the valve combinations given.

Chromatic scale starting on C♯ (two octaves, from memory) (tempo, dynamics and articulation as for scales below)</td></tr>
<tr><td colspan="5">Candidate to prepare in full either Section ii) or Section iii)</td></tr>
<tr><td colspan="5">either ii) Scales & Arpeggios (from memory) − the examiner will select from the following:</td></tr>
<tr>
<td>Candidates should prepare scales and arpeggios from the following tonal centres:
C major, C minor
F♯ major, F♯ minor

Plus:
Crabwise scale from C and G
Whole-tone scale starting on C and F♯
Dominant 7th in the keys of F and B
Diminished 7th starting on C and F♯
Augmented arpeggio starting on C and F♯
Chromatic scale starting on C and F♯</td>
<td>two octaves</td>
<td>♩ = 88-132</td>
<td>tongued, slurred or staccato-tongued as requested by the examiner</td>
<td>f or mf or p or cresc./dim. (p-f-p) or dim./cresc. (f-p-f)</td>
</tr>
<tr><td colspan="5">When the examiner requests a major tonal centre, the candidate should play in succession:
    The major scale
    The major arpeggio

When the examiner requests a minor tonal centre, the candidate should play in succession:
    The melodic minor scale
    The harmonic minor scale
    The minor arpeggio</td></tr>
<tr><td colspan="5">or iii) Orchestral and brass band extracts
See current syllabus for details</td></tr>
</table>

i) Lip flexibility exercise

Repeat (descending) using the following valve combinations:

2nd (1st and 2nd) − 1st (open) − 2nd and 3rd (1st)

Tuba only:

Repeat (descending) using the following valve combinations:

1st − 2nd and 3rd − 1st, 2nd and 3rd

Grade 8 continued

Chromatic scale starting on C# (two octaves)

ii) Scales & arpeggios

C major scale (two octaves)

C major arpeggio (two octaves)

C harmonic minor scale (two octaves)

C melodic minor scale (two octaves)

C minor arpeggio (two octaves)

Chromatic scale starting on C (two octaves)

Whole-tone scale starting on C (two octaves)

Augmented arpeggio starting on C (two octaves)

Diminished 7th starting on C (two octaves)

Dominant 7th in the key of F (two octaves)

F# major scale (two octaves)

F# major arpeggio (two octaves)

Grade 8 continued

F# harmonic minor scale (two octaves)

F# melodic minor scale (two octaves)

F# minor arpeggio (two octaves)

Chromatic scale starting on F# (two octaves)

Whole-tone scale starting on F# (two octaves)

Augmented arpeggio starting on F# (two octaves)

Diminished 7th starting on F# (two octaves)

Dominant 7th in the key of B (two octaves)

Crabwise scale from C (two octaves – tongued *or* slurred as indicated)

Crabwise scale from G (two octaves – tongued *or* slurred as indicated)